LO♥E

BY **Stacy McAnulty**

ILLUSTRATED BY
Joanne Lew-Vriethoff

SCHOLASTIC INC.

ISBN 978-1-338-61241-7

12 11 10 9 8 7 6 5 4 3 2 1   19 20 21 22 23 24

Printed in the U.S.A.   76

This edition first printing, September 2019

Print book cover and interior design by T. L. Bonaddio

For Kristen-S. M.

For Stacy, Teresa, and Julie,
family, much LOVE-J. L. V.

Love is . . .

a fancy dinner.

Love needs
special presents.

And designer greeting cards.

Love calls for bouquets of flowers.

And must have the finest chocolate.

Love sounds
like poetry.

Love comes in the shape of a heart.

And sparkles like diamonds.

Love happens
at first sight.

And needs the tightest hugs.

Because nothing else matters without . . .

LOVE.